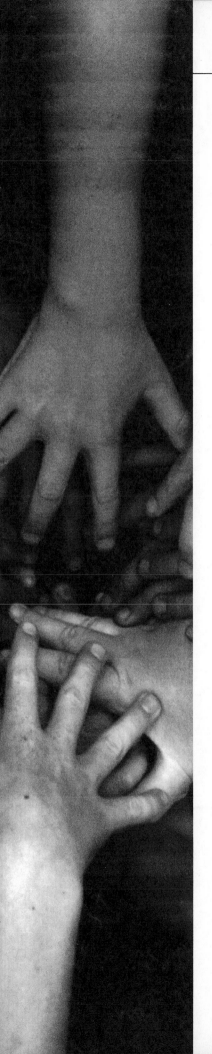

# *Social Studies Alive!*®
## My School and Family

**TCi**™

Chief Executive Officer: Bert Bower

Chief Operating Officer: Amy Larson

Director of Product Development: Liz Russell

Managing Editor: Laura Alavosus

Editorial Project Manager: Lara Fox

Project Editor: Beverly Cory

Editorial Associates: Anna Embree and Sarah Sudano

Production Manager: Lynn Sanchez

Design Manager: Jeff Kelly

Graphic Designer: Cheri DeBusk

Photo Edit Manager: Margee Robinson

Photo Editor: Diane Austin

Art Editor: Sarah Wildfang

Audio Manager: Katy Haun

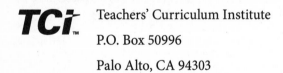

Teachers' Curriculum Institute

P.O. Box 50996

Palo Alto, CA 94303

Customer Service: 800-497-6138

www.teachtci.com

ISBN 978-1-58371-777-6

2 3 4 5 6 7 8 9 10 -QW- 15 14 13 12 11 10 09

# Acknowledgments

**Program Director**

Bert Bower

**Program Consultant**

Vicki LaBoskey, Ph.D., Professor of Education,
Mills College, Oakland, California

**Student Edition Writers**

Laura M. Alavosus

Abigail Boyce

Susan Buckley

Beverly Cory

Wendy Frey

**Curriculum Developers**

Joyce Bartky

Nicolle Hutchinson

**Reading Specialist**

Barbara Schubert, Ph.D., Reading Specialist,
Saint Mary's College, Moraga, California

**Teacher and Content Consultants**

Jill Bartky, Teacher, Sharp Park Elementary
School, Pacifica, California

Debra Elsen, Teacher, Manchester Elementary,
Manchester, Maryland

Gina Frazzini, Literary Coach, Gatzert
Elementary, Seattle, Washington

Patrick J. Lee, Teacher, Ohlone Elementary,
Palo Alto, California

Jennifer Miley, Teacher, Duveneck Elementary
School, Palo Alto, California

Mitch Pascal, Social Studies Specialist, Arlington
County Schools, Arlington, Virginia

Jodi Perraud, Teacher, Boulevard Heights
Elementary, Hollywood, Florida

Becky Suthers, Retired Teacher, Stephen F. Austin
Elementary, Weatherford, Texas

**Literature Consultant**

Regina M. Rees, Ph.D., Assistant Professor,
Beeghly College of Education, Youngstown State
University, Youngstown, Ohio

**Music Specialist**

Beth Yankee, Teacher, The Woodward School for
Technology and Research, Kalamazoo, Michigan

**Maps**

Mapping Specialists, Ltd. Madison, Wisconsin

# Contents

# Contents

These two goats cannot pass on the bridge.

What will happen next? Draw your ideas.

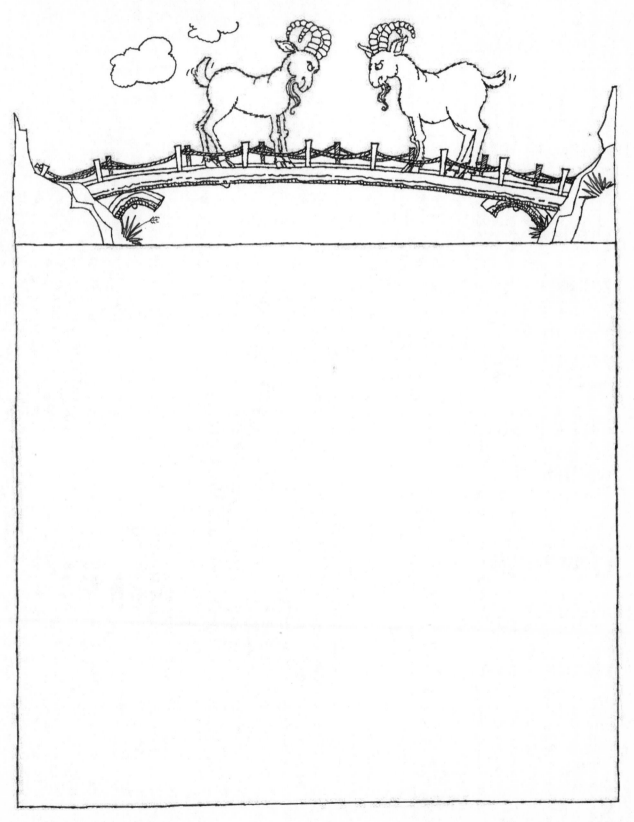

# 1

Circle 2 ways

we share.

Circle 2 ways

we talk.

Circle 2 ways

we listen.

Circle 2 ways

we take turns.

How Do We Get Along in School? **3**

# 1

How can you make this lot a place to share?

Draw what your class chooses to do.

Our _____

What else can we do to get along in school?

Draw a picture. Write a sentence.

First answer the questions for yourself.

Then shake hands with a friend.

Say hello. Ask the same questions.

| | | Me | Classmate |
|---|---|---|---|
| | Do you like to dance? | | |
| | Are you a girl? | | |
| | Do you feel happy today? | | |
| | Are you 6 years old? | | |
| | Are you a boy? | | |
| | Do you like to draw? | | |
| | Do you like sports? | | |
| | Have you lost a tooth? | | |

# 2

Write a word in each blank. Draw a picture for each pair of sentences.

## Part A

Each of us is special.

_____ makes me special.

## Part B

We are good at different things.

I am good at _____ .

## Part C

> You can learn from me.
>
> I can help you _____ .

## Part D

> I can learn from you.
>
> You can help me _____ .

# 2   It is summer. What is the grasshopper doing?

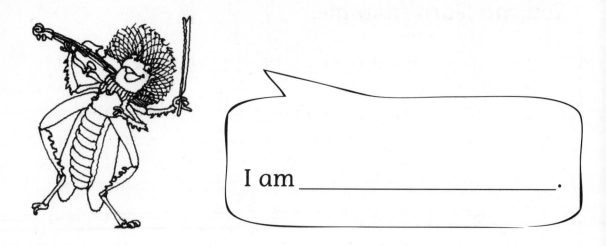

I am _____.

Now it is winter. How does the grasshopper feel?

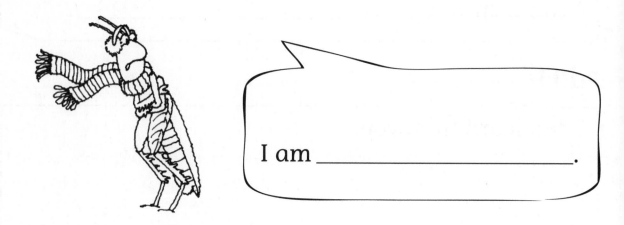

I am _____.

What did the grasshopper learn from the ant?

Look in your book to find the lesson.

_____

_____

Think of a different lesson.

Let's say the ant learned from the grasshopper.

The grasshopper was good at something.

What was it? What could the ant have learned?

I am good at _____.

I can help you learn _____

_____.

# 2

Write your partner's name on Student

Handout 2C. Color the gift. Follow this key.

Is your partner a boy or a girl?

Use the matching crayon.

Color the ribbon on the gift.

Girl

Boy

# What does your partner like to do?

Use the key to color the rest of the gift.

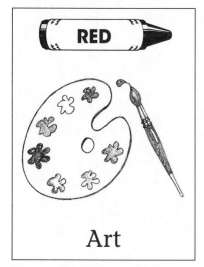

Art

Music

Talking

Athletics

Solving problems

Make-believe

Reading

What is one rule in your home?

Draw a picture.

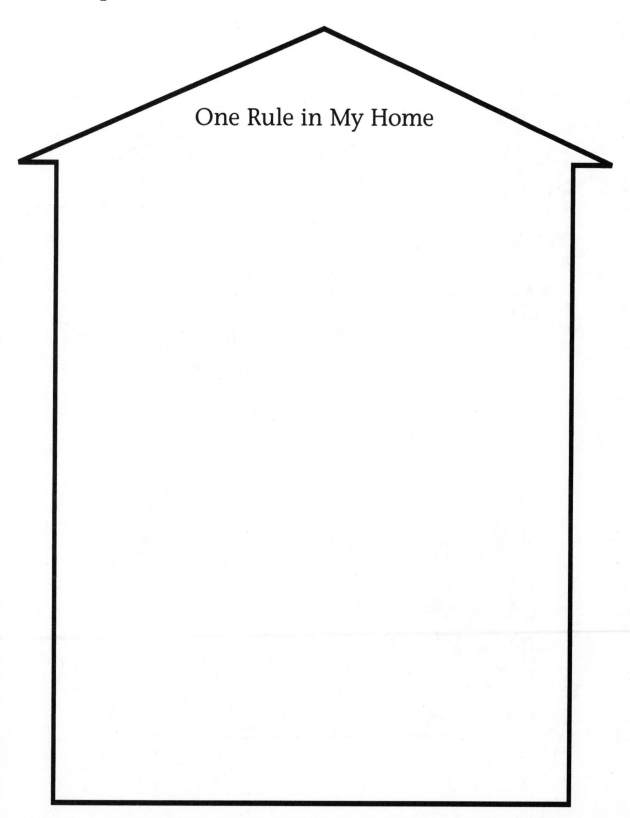

One Rule in My Home

# 3

Where are all the children getting along?

Circle the picture.

Where are the children being safe?

Circle the picture.

# 3

Where are the children being fair?

Circle the picture.

Where are the children learning?

Circle the picture.

# 3

These children had a meeting at City Hall.

They voted for two rules. Circle the two rules.

- Dogs must be on a leash.

- Anyone on a bike must use the bike lane.

- No one can set off fireworks.

- Do not run in the halls.

- Children on bikes must wear helmets.

This rule helps us

be safe.

What is another rule that helps us be safe on city streets?

Draw a picture.

# 3

## What is one class rule? Write it here:

Draw what happens when you follow the rule.

# What if you break this rule? Draw what may happen.

Who helps you at your school? Draw a picture.

# 4 Choose a word to match each picture.

---

## Word Bank

Principal     Secretary     Custodian     Teacher

---

_____

_____

_____

_____

Read each riddle. Who can help with
the problem? Draw a line to that person.

1. I am sick today.
   Who should Dad
   call at school?

2. My friend spilled
   her milk. Who can
   help clean it up?

3. My mom wants to know
   about school rules.
   Who should she ask?

4. I want to learn about
   animals. Who can
   help me?

Look at the chart. Do you know these leaders?

| Leader | Symbol | Role | One thing this leader does |
|--------|--------|------|----------------------------|
| Mayor | | Head of a city | Looks after city streets and parks |
| Governor | | Head of a state | Gets help for people in floods |
| President | | Head of a country | Helps make laws for the United States |

Listen to each riddle on the next page.

Use the chart above to find the answer.

**4**

1. When there are floods, I get help for the people in my state.

I am the _____ .

2. I am the leader of the United States.

I am the _____ .

3. If your city streets need fixing, you can talk to me.

I am the _____ .

Look at your handout.

1. Who is the helper on your page? Circle one.

Teacher      Principal      Secretary      Custodian

2. Think about a person who does this job in your

   school. What is this person's name?

   _____

3. Draw some ideas for your page.

┌─────────────────────────────────────────────┐
│                                               │
│                                               │
│                                               │
│                                               │
│                                               │
│                                               │
│                                               │
│                                               │
│                                               │
│                                               │
└─────────────────────────────────────────────┘

What is one way you help others at home?

Write or draw what you do.

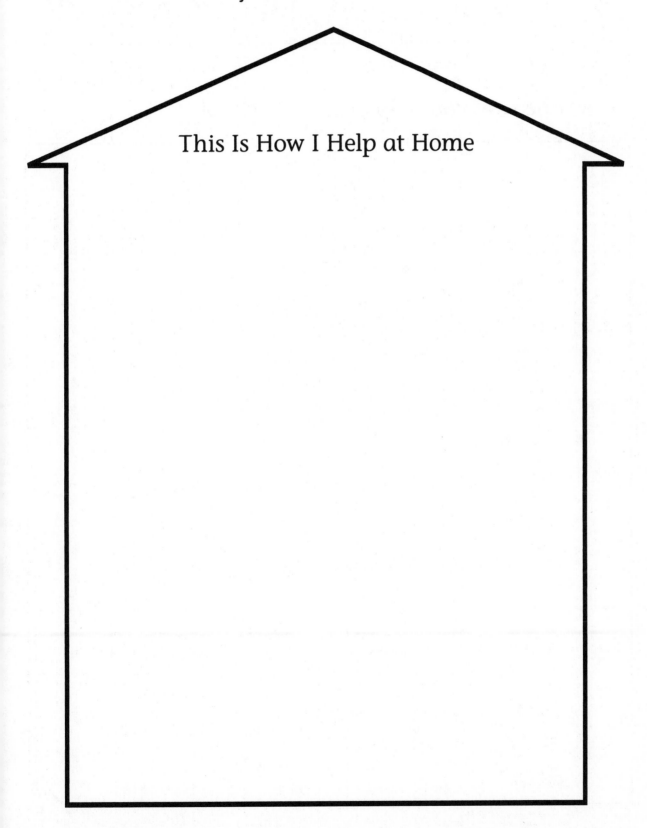

This Is How I Help at Home

# 5

List two ways you help others at school.

1. _____

2. _____


Draw one way you help others at school.

List two ways you take care of your things

at school.

1. _____

2. _____


Draw one way you take care of your things at school.

# 5

List two ways you do your best at school.

1. _____

2. _____


Draw one way you do your best at school.

List two ways you respect others at school.

1. _____

2. _____

Draw one way you respect others at school.

# 5 Part A

Clara Barton lived long ago. She lived by
the Golden Rule. List three things that
Clara did to help people.

1. _____

2. _____

3. _____

## Part B

Look at the pictures of Clara Barton in your book.

What is one way that life in the past was different?

Draw or write your answer.

## Part C

If Clara were alive today, in what ways

might her life be the same?

Hint: Think about the ways that she helped people.

Draw a picture of yourself working with Clara.

What are you both doing? Who are you helping?

# 5

Think about the Helping Hand
Award you will make.

Who is a good helper at your school?

_____

How is that person a good helper?

_____

See the person in your mind. What is your helper
doing? Who is being helped? Draw some ideas. Use
your drawings on your award.

Have you ever seen maps like these?

What do you think they show? Write your ideas.

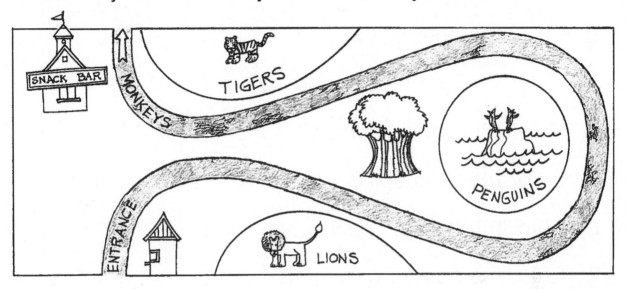

This map shows _____.

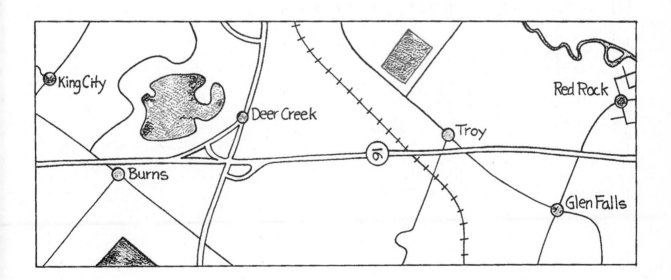

This map shows _____.

# 6

Color the map. Follow these steps:

1. Draw a brown line around the classroom.

2. Color the door orange.

3. Color the round tables green.

4. Color the cabinet orange.

5. Color the teacher's desk brown.

6. Color the student desks blue.

7. Color the recess basket yellow.

8. Color the computer black.

9. Color the rectangular table red.

10. Color the symbols in the map key to match your map.

# Map of Ms. Hutchinson's Classroom

## Map Key

| | |
|---|---|
| Door | / |
| Round table | ○ |
| Cabinet | ▯ |
| Teacher's desk | ▢ |
| Student desk | ▭ |
| Recess basket | ○ |
| Rectangular table | ▯ |
| Computer | ◰ |

N E
W S

Look at the maps on the next page.

Choose words to fill in the blanks below.

1. I want to find what is north of my state.

I need a _____ map.

2. I want to find the school nurse's office.

I need a _____ map.

3. I want to find City Hall.

I need a _____ map.

4. I want to find Africa, where elephants live.

I need a _____ map.

## School Map

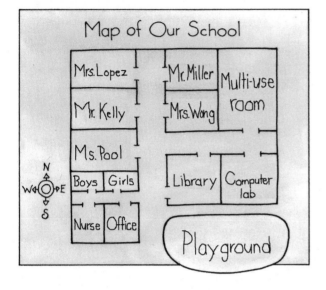

## Town Map

## United States Map

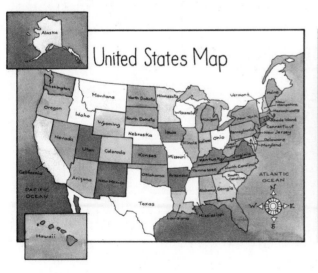

## World Map

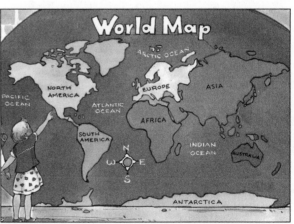

# 6

Make a new classroom map. Use the symbols on Student Handout 6.

1. Color each symbol.

2. Cut out each symbol.

3. Glue the symbols on the map.
   Make this classroom look different!

4. Color the map key to match your map.

5. Write the letters N, S, E, and W on the compass rose to point north, south, east, and west.

## Map Key

|  |  |
|--------|-------|
| / | Door |
| ◯ | Round table |
| ▭ | Cabinet |
| ▢ | Teacher's desk |
| ▭ | Student desk |
| ◯ | Recess basket |
| ▯ | Rectangular table |
| ▭ | Computer |

## Classroom Map

The past is all the time before today.

The past is last week. It is last year.

The past is when your parents
were young. It is when your
grandparents were young.

What does the past make you
think of? Draw a picture.

# 7

On the left, draw two objects you would find in a school long ago. On the right, draw two objects you would find in a school now.

| Schools Long Ago | Schools Now |
|---|---|
| 1 | 1 |
| 2 | 2 |

On the left, draw two objects children used in school long ago. On the right, draw two objects children use in school now.

| Student Life Long Ago | Student Life Now |
|---|---|
| **1** | **1** |
| **2** | **2** |

# 7

This is a timeline. It shows Mister Bob's long life. Add what he saw in his lifetime. Cut pictures from Student Handout 7. Glue them in order.

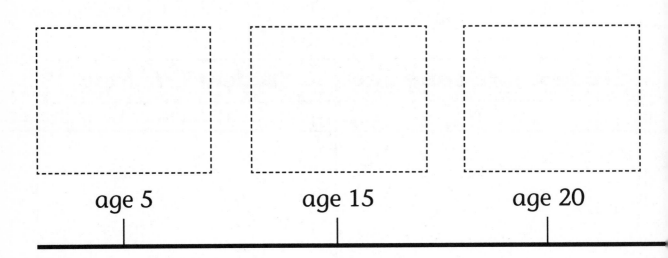

age 5        age 15        age 20

Make a timeline of your life. Guess what you will be doing in the future.

Draw a picture for each time. Write your age.

**My Past**

age _____

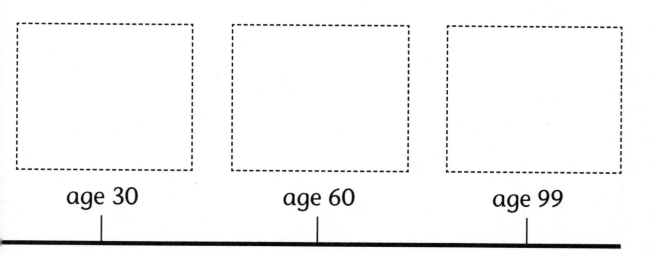

age 30        age 60        age 99

| | |
|---|---|
| **My Present** | **My Future** |

age _____        age _____

# 7

Things change over time. You read about schools of the past. Now think about schools of the future. Draw something that future schools might have.

How will this be used in future schools?

_____

_____

1. List something that you do with others.

_____

Draw a picture of what you do.

2. List something else that you do with others.

_____

Draw a picture of what you do.

# 8

Choose a word. Write it next to its picture.

Then write a sentence about that group.

| School | Family | Community |
|--------|--------|-----------|

_____

_____

_____

Gym

_____

_____

_____

_____

What have you learned from your family group?

Finish the sentence. Tell one thing you learned from your family. Name the family member who taught you. Then draw a picture to go with your sentence.

I learned _____

from my_____.

**8** Draw a school group that you belong to.

Write what you are doing in the picture.

_____

_____

Draw a family group that you belong to.

Write what you are doing in the picture.

_____

_____

# 8

Draw a community group that you belong to.

Write what you are doing in the picture.

_____

_____

What is a family? What does the word mean to you? Fill in the word web. Write one word in each box.

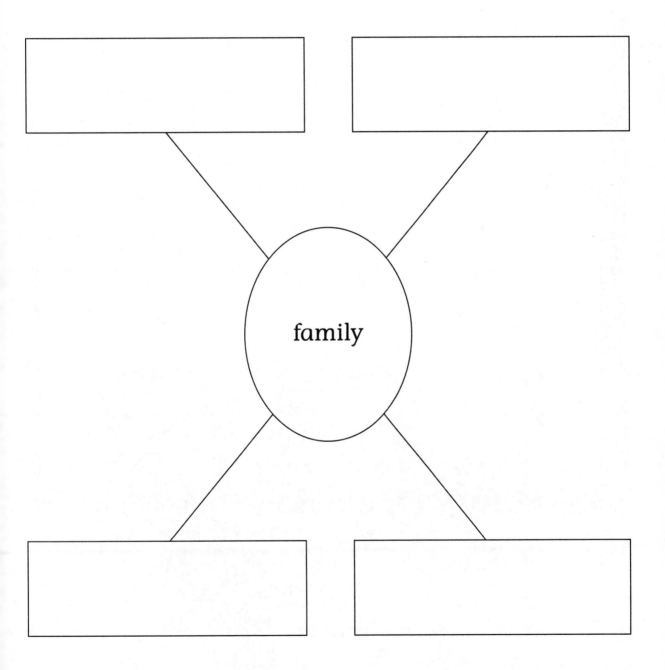

family

# 9

## Part A. Family Members

Name four different family members.

_____

_____

_____

_____

# 9

## Part B. Family Homes

Name three kinds of homes.

_____

_____

_____

# 9

## Part C. Family Activities

Name three family activities.

_____

_____

_____

Your family is special. The place where you live

is special, too. What makes it special? Draw a

picture postcard.

What could you write on your postcard?

Write about the place where you live.

How is it different from other places?

_____

_____

_____

What are some things that families buy?

Draw four things. Write the name of each one.

# 10

Draw a need in five boxes.

Draw a want in four boxes.

Label each drawing "need" or "want."

| **NEEDS AND WANTS BINGO** | | |
|---|---|---|
| **1** ____ | **2** ____ | **3** ____ |
| **4** ____ | **5** ____ | **6** ____ |
| **7** ____ | **8** ____ | **9** ____ |

Popcorn has a long trip from the field to the bowl. Think about all the workers who help it get there. Draw or write about at least four steps along the way. Number your steps in order.

In the end, a boy got something he wanted—popcorn. What did all the workers get?

# 10

You saw lots of needs and wants for camping.

Draw and label one need and one want.

Complete the sentences.

This is a need because

_____.

This is a want because

_____.

Write one word to answer each question.

Draw a picture.

1. What does your family need to grow and stay healthy?

   _____

2. What does your family need to keep warm outdoors?

   _____

3. What does your family need to protect them from wind and rain?

   _____

# 11 Part A

Draw pictures to complete each sentence.

1. In my family, we help each other by

2. In my family, we share what we know by

## Part B

Draw pictures to complete each sentence.

1. In my family, we show feelings by

2. In my family, we spend time together by

# 11

## Plan a poster about taking care of Earth.

What is your pledge? _____

_____

_____

Think about the scroll you will make.

Draw or write some ideas for your scroll.

1. How can you help your family with chores?

2. How can you share what you know with your family?

3. How can you show that you care about your family?

Think about your family over the past few years.

What is one thing that has changed?

_____

_____

Draw a picture to show that change.

# 12 Part A

Think about how life will change when you are older.

1. What new chores will you have? Draw a chore you

   will do when you are older.

2. What new things will you be able to do? Draw

   something you will do when you are older.

## Part B

Write two sentences about how Ted's family has changed.

1. _____

_____

_____

2. _____

_____

_____

# 12

Families change over time. So do ways of life.

Next to each picture, draw what we use today.

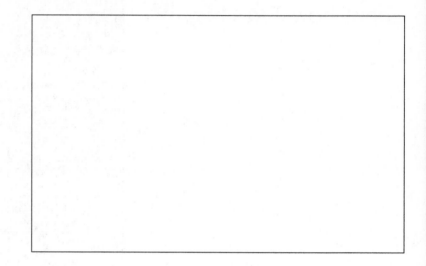

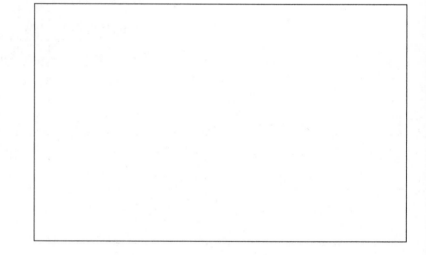

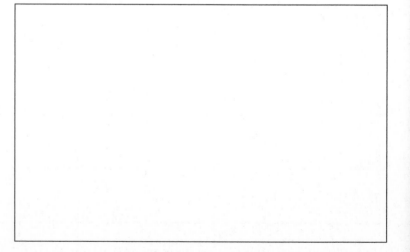

Draw a picture of your family now.

Draw a picture of your family in the future.

Glue shutter here

Glue shutter here

Draw one picture for each holiday.

Fourth of July

Valentine's Day

Thanksgiving

# 13 Draw a picture of Roberto's birthday party.

Write one way Roberto's birthday is different from yours.

Draw a picture of the Chinese Lantern Festival.

Write one thing you learned about this festival.

Choose one of the places you read about.

Finish the travel poster. Write

- the name of the place.

- one tradition in that place.

Then draw a picture. Use your book for ideas.

Come to _____

where _____ is a tradition.

# 13 What could you draw on your quilt square? List or draw some ideas. Choose a special day:

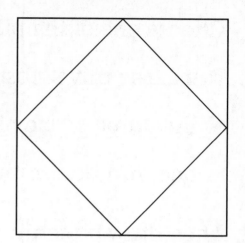

| Food | Activities |
|------|------------|
| What do you eat? | What do you do? |

| Clothes | Decorations |
|---------|-------------|
| What do you wear? | What makes things pretty? |

Draw your home in the center.

Draw four places near your home. Label them.

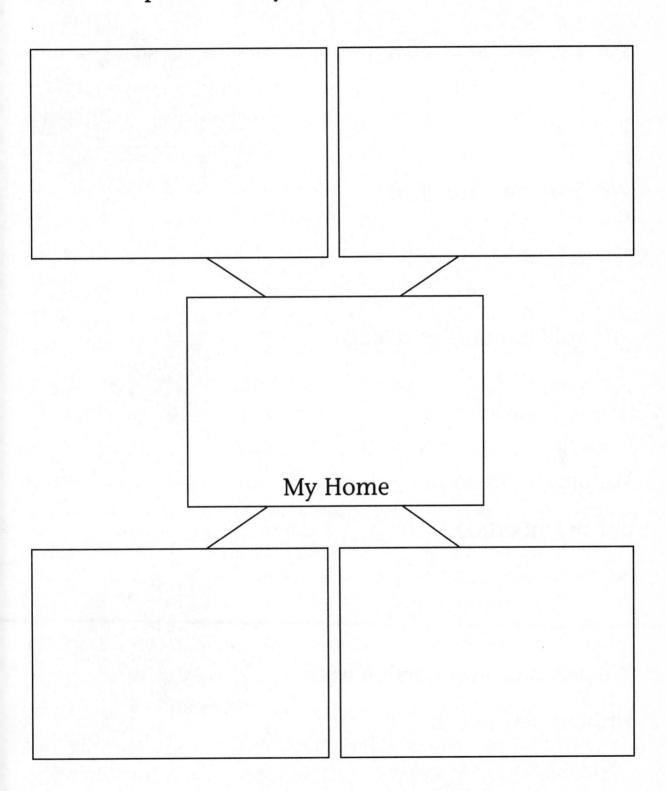

My Home

# 14 Circle sentences that describe a good neighbor.

We say hello to our neighbors.

We keep our yard clean.

We walk our dog on a leash.

We pick up trash in
our neighborhood.

We pick our neighbors' flowers
without permission.

We let our dog run in our
neighbor's yard.

We wave to our neighbors.

We water our neighbors' plants
when they go away.

We feed our neighbors' pets
when they go away.

We drop trash on the street.

# 14

Good neighbors help each other.

Read these two problems.

Write your ideas for

helping out.

The fence is broken.
Now my geese are lost!

I love my new puppy.
But I still get lonely.

Choose one problem. How could a neighbor help?

_____

_____

_____

Give yourself an award.

Draw yourself being a good neighbor.

Write what you did.

_____

_____

_____

# Credits

## Photographs

**Front Cover**
Ableimages/Getty Images

**Title Page**
Ableimages/Getty Images

**Chapter 3**
**20:** Courtesy of the City of Bellflower, CA

**Chapter 4**
**26 T:** RF/Getty Images **26 CT:** Michael Malyszko/Getty Images **26 CB:** Patti McConville/Getty Images **26 B:** Bruce Ayres/Getty Images

**Chapter 12**
**78 T:** Culver Pictures, Inc./SuperStock **78 C:** RF/Corbis **78 B:** Petrified Collection-The Image Bank/Getty Images

## Art

**Chapter 1**
**1:** Doug Roy **2 L:** Doug Roy **2 R:** DJ Simison **4:** Doug Roy

**Chapter 2**
**7:** Doug Roy **10:** Jon Goodell **11:** Jon Goodell **12:** Doug Roy **13:** Doug Roy

**Chapter 3**
**16:** Susan Jaekel **17:** Susan Jaekel **18:** Susan Jaekel **19:** Susan Jaekel **21:** Doug Roy

**Chapter 4**
**27:** Gary Undercuffler **28:** Doug Roy

**Chapter 5**
**38:** Doug Roy

**Chapter 6**
**39:** Doug Roy **43:** Len Ebert

**Chapter 7**
**47:** Doug Roy

**Chapter 8**
**54:** Carol Newsome **56:** Doug Roy **57:** Doug Roy **58:** Doug Roy

**Chapter 9**
**60:** Jane McCreary **61:** Jane McCreary **62:** Jane McCreary

**Chapter 12**
**77:** DJ Simison

**Chapter 13**
**82:** Dennis Hockerman

**Chapter 14**
**86:** Len Ebert **87:** Len Ebert **88:** Susan Jaekel

Artists represented by Ann Remen-Willis, Artist Representative and Art Manager:

Len Ebert
Jon Goodell
Dennis Hockerman
Susan Jaekel
Jane McCreary
Carol Newsome
Doug Roy
DJ Simison
Gary Undercuffler